Top Tunes for Flute

Kevin Mayhew

We hope you enjoy *Top Tunes for Flute*.
Further copies of this and the other books in the series
are available from your local music shop.

In case of difficulty, please contact the publisher direct:

The Sales Department
KEVIN MAYHEW LTD
Buxhall
Stowmarket
Suffolk IP14 3DJ

Phone 01449 737978
Fax 01449 737834

Please ask for our complete catalogue of outstanding Instrumental Music.

Acknowledgements

The publishers wish to express their gratitude to the copyright owners for
permission to use copyright material in this book. Details of these are given
underneath the individual tunes. All other tunes are copyright Kevin Mayhew Ltd.

Every effort has been made to trace the owners of copyright material, and we hope
that no copyright has been infringed. Pardon is sought and apology made if the
contrary be the case, and a correction will be made in any reprint of this book.

First published in Great Britain in 1996 by Kevin Mayhew Ltd.

© Copyright 1996 Kevin Mayhew Ltd.

ISBN 0 86209 816 5
Catalogue No: 3611199

Front cover illustration by Neil Pinchbeck
Cover design by Graham Johnstone and Veronica Ward

Music arrangements by Donald Thomson
Music Editor: Stephanie Hill
Music setting by Daniel Kelly

Printed and bound in Great Britain

Contents

THIS OLD MAN
Anon.

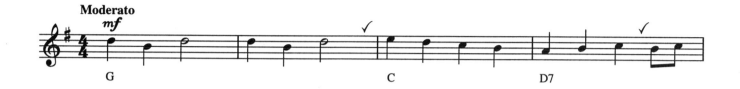

OH SUSANNA
Stephen Foster (1826-1864)

LITTLE BROWN JUG

R A Eastburn

J'AI DU BON TABAC

Traditional French Melody

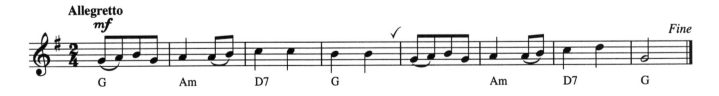

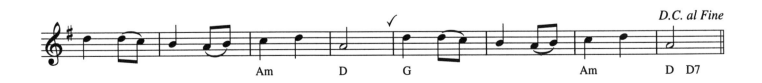

KUM BA YAH
Traditional Angolan Melody

THERE IS A GREEN HILL
William Horsley (1774-1858)

TALLIS' CANON
Thomas Tallis (1505-1585)

THE GRAND OLD DUKE OF YORK

Traditional English Melody

LONDON'S BURNING

Traditional English Melody

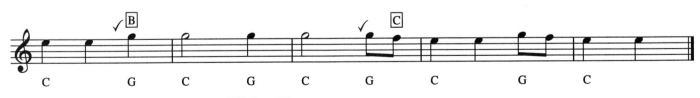

This may be played as a round with entries at A B and C

CAMPTOWN RACES

Stephen Foster (1826-1864)

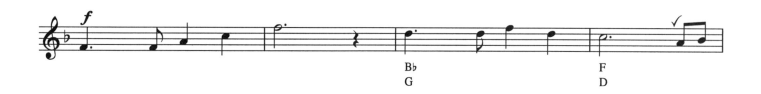

HERE WE GO ROUND THE MULBERRY BUSH

Traditional English Melody

SCARBOROUGH FAIR
Traditional Irish Melody

ON TOP OF OLD SMOKEY
Traditional American Melody

CLEMENTINE

Percy Montrose

ON ILKLEY MOOR BAHT 'AT

Traditional English Melody

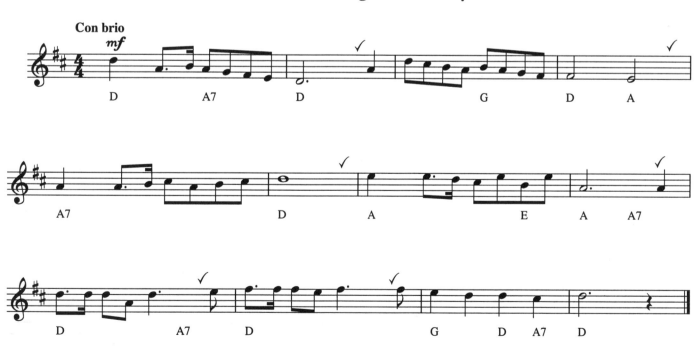

GO DOWN, MOSES

Spiritual

AMAZING GRACE

Traditional American Melody

DOWN BY THE RIVERSIDE

Spiritual

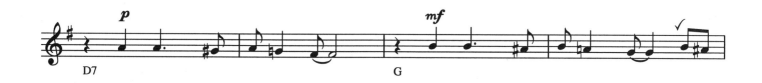

ALL THROUGH THE NIGHT

Traditional Welsh Melody

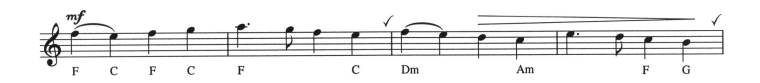

MARCH from 'SCIPIO'

George Frideric Handel (1685-1759)

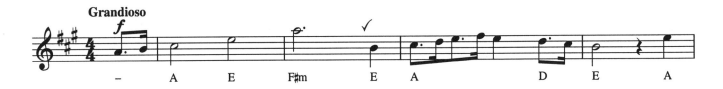

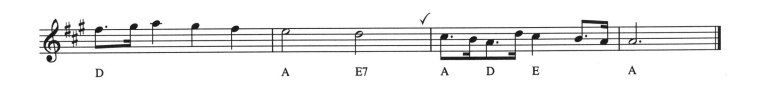

GREENSLEEVES

Anonymous 17th Century Melody

MEMORY from 'CATS'

Andrew Lloyd Webber (*b.*1948)

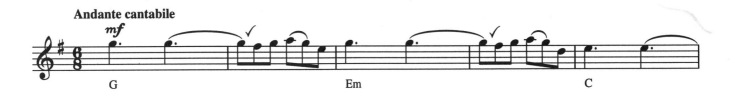

THE KEEL ROW

Traditional English Melody

THE DRUNKEN SAILOR
Sea Shanty

THE BLUE BELL OF SCOTLAND
Traditional Scottish Melody

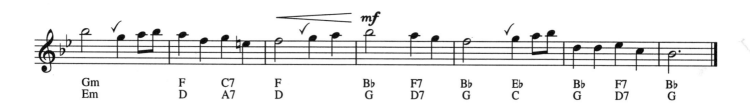

SHEEP MAY SAFELY GRAZE

Johann Sebastian Bach (1685-1750)

PAVANE

Gabriel Fauré (1845-1924)

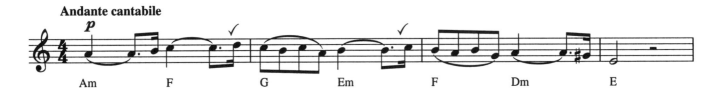

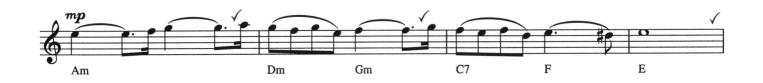

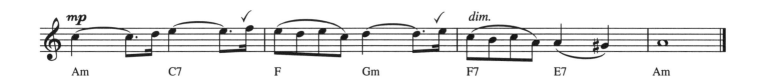

HOME, SWEET HOME

Henry Bishop

POLOVTSIAN DANCE

Alexander Borodin (1833-1887)

OH DEAR, WHAT CAN THE MATTER BE?

Traditional Melody

JUPITER from 'THE PLANETS'

Gustav Holst (1874-1934)

BILLY BOY
Sea Shanty

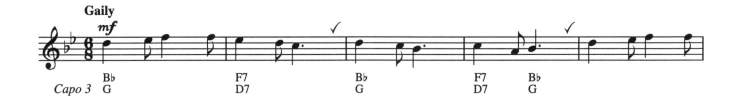

NEW WORLD SYMPHONY (2nd Movement)
Antonin Dvorak (1841-1904)

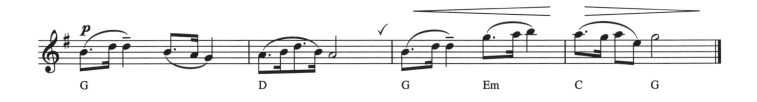

MINUET

Johann Sebastian Bach (1685-1750)

VALSE LENTE from 'COPPÉLIA'

Léo Delibes (1836-1891)

COUNTRY GARDENS

Traditional English Melody

Capo 2

A	D	E	A	Bm	E7	A
G	C	D	G	Am	D7	G

D	E	A	Bm	E7	A
C	D	G	Am	D7	G

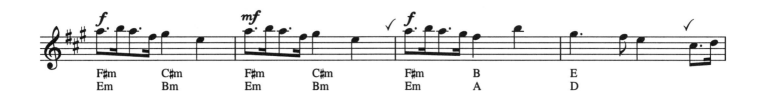

F#m	C#m	F#m	C#m	F#m	B	E
Em	Bm	Em	Bm	Em	A	D

A	D	E	A	Bm	E7	A
G	C	D	G	Am	D7	G

THERE IS A TAVERN IN THE TOWN

Traditional English Melody

Capo 3

–	Bb	F7
–	G	D7

Bb	Eb	F7	Bb
G	C	D7	G

SPRING from 'THE FOUR SEASONS'

Antonio Vivaldi (1678-1741)

LAND OF HOPE AND GLORY

Edward Elgar (1875- 1934)

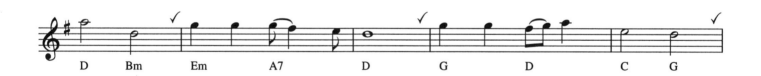

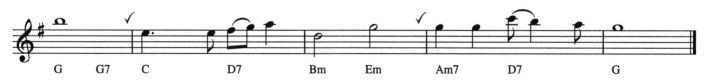

TAMBOURIN

François-Joseph Gossec (1734-1829)

GLORY, GLORY HALLELUJAH

William Stäffe

ALL PEOPLE THAT ON EARTH DO DWELL

From the 'Genevan Psalter'

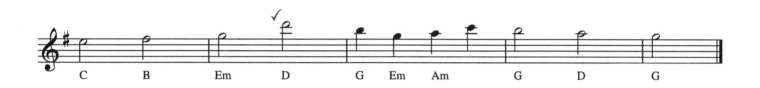

THEME from 'THE TOY SYMPHONY'

Leopold Mozart (1756-1791)

LARGO

George Frideric Handel (1685-1759)

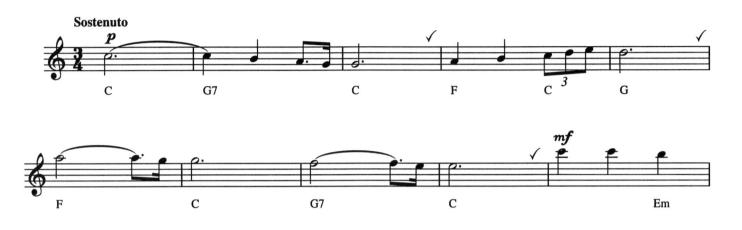

ETON BOATING SONG

Traditional English Melody

EARLY ONE MORNING
Traditional English Melody

DANCE OF THE HOURS
Amilcare Ponchielli (1834-1886)

THE LAST ROSE OF SUMMER

Traditional Irish Melody

MARCHE MILITAIRE

Franz Schubert (1797-1828)

RULE, BRITANNIA
Thomas Arne (1710-1778)

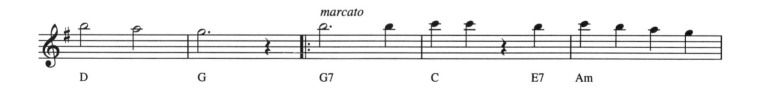